ANTONÍN DVOŘÁK

QUAR

for 2 Violins, Viola

F major/F-Dur/Fa majeur

Op. 96

'American'

Ernst Eulenburg Ltd

London · Mainz · Madrid · New York · Paris · Prague · Tokyo · Toronto · Zürich

ANTONIN DVOŘÁK
String Quartet in F major, Op. 96

This quartet, sometimes known as 'The American', was written inside a fortnight in June 1893 while Dvořák and his family were staying in the Czech settlement at Spilleville, Iowa. At the end of the score he wrote: 'Thanks be to God. I am satisfied: it went quickly'. The pentatonic themes bear some resemblance to negro spirituals, but no quotations have been discovered. The violin theme in the third movement, bars 21 – 28, is based on a birdsong Dvořák heard in the woods near Spilleville. According to John Clapham[1] the bird must have been a scarlet tanager. Bar 17 in the slow movement has always been printed wrongly: in this edition the fifth note in the cello part has been corrected from E to D (cf bar 9).

Roger Fiske, 1972

Streichquartett in F-Dur, Op. 96

Dieses, auch als das „Amerikanische" bekannte Quartett, entstand innerhalb von vierzehn Tagen im Juni 1893. Dvořák weilte damals mit seiner Familie in der tschechischen Siedlung in Spilleville, im Staate Iowa. Am Ende der Partitur schrieb er die Worte: „Gott sei Dank. Ich bin zufrieden: es ging schnell." Die pentatonischen Themen ähneln in gewisser Beziehung den *Spirituals* der Neger, doch haben sich keine direkten Zitate ermitteln lassen. Das Geigenthema im dritten Satz, T. 21 – 28, beruht auf einem Vogelgesang, den Dvořák in den Wäldern um Spilleville gehört hat. John Clapham behauptet[1], es müsse sich dabei um einen *scarlet tanager (Piranga erythromelas)* gehandelt haben. T. 17 im langsamen Satz ist von je falsch im Druck erschienen. In der vorliegenden Ausgabe ist die fünfte Note in der Cellostimme korrigiert worden (D anstatt E, vgl. T. 9).

Übersetzung Stefan de Haan

[1] *Antonin Dvořák, Musician and Craftsman* (London, 1966) p. 181

Quartet

I

Antonin Dvořák, Op. 96
1841-1904

E. E. 6017   Ernst Eulenburg & Co. GmbH.

in tempo

II

18

E. E. 6017

III

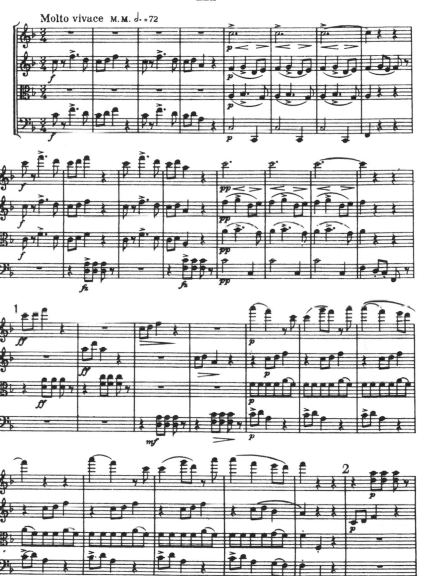

molto rit. in tempo

Da Capo al Fine

28

Finale

IV

Vivace ma non troppo M.M. ♩ = 152

E. E. 6017

E. E. 6017

8 Meno mosso

sul G

34